698
C

WOOD LAMINATING

WOOD LAMINATING

J. HUGH CAPRON

Professor of Industrial Arts

Winona State College

Winona, Minnesota

McKNIGHT & McKNIGHT PUBLISHING COMPANY

Bloomington

Illinois

PREFACE

This book has been written for the use of industrial arts students, teachers, and for the home craftsman.

It is the result of several years of experimentation and the collection of countless details about the wood laminating industry. Although this industry is young, it is making a greater and greater impact on allied fields.

The growth of the laminating industry has certainly not reached maturity and with this expansion comes the responsibility of industrial arts to relate the technology of this industry to the oncoming generations of students who will be challenged and intrigued by the innumerable things that can be accomplished with a basic natural resource, wood.

Wood laminating offers ideal opportunities for *problem solving, research projects,* and *experimentation.* Possible topics may be found in the Index under *Quality, factors affecting.* Each has variations to try, measure, and evaluate.

For the home craftsman, wood laminating is a fascinating and unusual hobby. With a few basic tools and the information obtained from this book, he will be able to design and build with wood laminates.

Each of the projects presented in Section II has been developed with the learner in mind. In each case, the laminated portion was selected as a part of the design because it fulfills a functional purpose better than other materials.

Although the drawing describes the project in detail, variations in each of the designs are normally possible. These projects should and will be suggestive of many others. The beginner will achieve greatest success with the simpler forms, while more experienced workers can design their own projects and improvise the necessary forms to produce them.

ACKNOWLEDGMENTS

The author is indebted to the following individuals for their advice and assistance in the writing of this text:

William S. Dawley, Mechanical Engineer (Retired),
Winona, Minnesota

James Spear, Audio-Visual Specialist,
Winona State College, Winona, Minnesota

The following commercial firms generously provided advice, materials, and illustrations:

Rilco Laminated Products, Inc., St. Paul, Minnesota
The Borden Company, New York, New York
Bancroft Sporting Goods Company, Pawtucket, Rhode Island
Brunswick-Balke-Collender Company, Chicago, Illinois
Northland Ski Company, St. Paul, Minnesota
Ben Pearson, Inc. Pine Bluff, Arkansas
H. R. Smith Company, Canby, Oregon
Wilson Sporting Goods Company, River Grove, Illinois
Herman Miller Company, Zeeland, Michigan
Thonet Industries, Inc., New York, New York
Taft Marine Woodcraft, Minneapolis, Minnesota
Higgins Corporation, New Orleans, Louisiana
Reeves Electronics, Inc., Chicago, Illinois
Adjustable Clamp Company, Chicago, Illinois
Goodyear Tire and Rubber Company, Akron, Ohio
Binks Manufacturing Company, Chicago, Illinois
Porter-Cable Company, Syracuse, New York
Skill Corporation, Chicago, Illinois
Masonite Corporation, Chicago, Illinois
A. G. Spalding and Brothers, Chicopee, Massachusetts

CONTENTS

INTRODUCTION

The practice of laminating wood, which has been known since the 15th century B. C., is currently an important process in modern industry. It is used in the manufacture of such things as tennis rackets, golf clubs, baseball bats, furniture, and rafters for large buildings.

In general, wood laminating consists of gluing parallel-grained layers of wood together in such a way as to produce an assembled piece of wood which has strength and shape characteristics that the original material did not have. A typical example of this process is the laminated roof arches pictured in Fig. 1. This shows a school gymnasium with the roof supported by a series of radial laminated arches. In this particular building, the rafters

Fig. 1. Laminated Rafters (Rilco)

9

span 84 feet. They are made from 13 plys of 2″ x 5″ Douglas Fir bonded together with water-resistant glue, and spaced twelve feet between centers. Note the absence of center structural supports that would hamper vision and restrict the playing area.

In laminated wood, the laminates are assembled so that all layers have the same grain direction. In contrast to this, plywood is assembled so that the grain of adjacent layers is at right angles. Fig. 2 clearly pictures this difference.

The advantages of using the wood laminating method are many. However, there are two primary reasons why the process has become so prominent in recent years. *First,* manufacturers of wood products have experienced increasing difficulty in obtaining top quality solid wood with adequate dimensions for their products. In these cases, there was little choice but to use a substitute material or to adapt the wood laminating process to the product. *Secondly,* the development of new wood adhesives which have high strength characteristics and a phenomenal resistance to weathering have made it practical to use laminated assemblies out-of-doors.

Fig. 2. Plywood (Top) and Laminated Wood (Below)

Wood laminates also have many less apparent advantages over other materials. For example, laminated wood structural members have a high resistance to corrosion and they are non-magnetic. Their resistance to corrosion makes them suitable for use in industrial buildings where the corrosive fumes cause rapid deterioration of steel structures. Wood laminates were ideal structural members for the well known non-magnetic mine sweepers used by the U. S. Navy.

Strangely enough, wood laminated beams and rafters offer certain advantages over steel in fire resistance.

Although the outsides of timbers tend to char badly, when exposed to fire, they will still retain a major portion of their strength for an extended period of time because of the slow rate at which large timbers burn. This may delay or prevent the collapse of a badly burned building.

In Fig. 3, the black beam of wood which appears as a horizontal member has been exposed to prolonged and intense heat that was adequate to distort the steel beams. In spite of this exposure, the timber still retained adequate strength to support the heavy "I" beams as they fell.

Fig. 3. Laminated Beams Support Twisted Steel (Borden)

PART

PRODUCTS,
MATERIALS,
EQUIPMENT, AND
PROCEDURES

WOOD LAMINATES IN INDUSTRY

Modern industry has made a wide variety of applications of wood laminating methods. A survey of wood laminated products will show many items made possible by developments in wood technology.

The products described in this chapter have been selected to be merely representative of the industry. They are not intended to be an inclusive list or description.

Sporting Goods

Baseball Bats

Although the modern baseball bat is frequently referred to as the "hickory" it is customarily made from second growth ash. In recent years, several firms have been experimenting with a bat made from laminated wood. It is their claim that a laminated bat can be designed and produced to exceed the rigid specifications of professionals.

Most of these laminated bats are assembled from two kinds of wood. As Fig. 4 indicates, they use a double core of hickory spaced and padded on each side with ash. This, they claim, is a nearly ideal combination of wood. Hickory is tough and somewhat heavier than ash, thus it makes a strong core for the ash barrel. By varying the thickness of each layer and the all-over shape, the balance of the bat can be controlled.

For many years the laminated baseball bat was declared illegal for major league play. More recently, the regulations have been modified to accept it at least on a temporary basis.

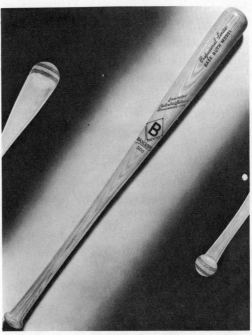

Fig. 4. Laminated Baseball Bat (Bancroft)

15

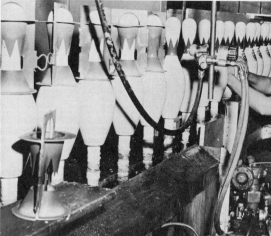

Fig. 5. Rough Turning a Bowling
Pin Billet (Brunswick)

Fig. 6. Spraying Finish on
Bowling Pins (Brunswick)

Bowling Pins

Laminated bowling pins were tested experimentally just after World War I and found to be practical for commercial use. It was not until the years following World War II, however, that shortages of hard maple encouraged manufacturers to attempt large-scale production of laminated pins.

Although the details of the manufacturing process differ, the basic procedure in producing a *laminated* pin involves more than 22 separate processes.

When the hard maple lumber first arrives at the mill for manufacture, it is graded and sorted according to the length and quality of the material. Since the moisture content is very critical, the lumber is stacked and placed in a forced draft kiln for a period of 50 to 60 days. During this period, the temperature and humidity of the kiln are rigidly controlled to produce stock with the correct moisture content and free from stresses.

After drying, the stock is sent to the roughing mill where defects are removed from the wood and billets of suitable size are made ready for the machine operations.

The term *billet,* as used in the woodworking trade, refers to a piece of wood from which a unit may be shaped or machined. In this case, it is a block five inches square and seventeen inches long, from which a single pin is turned. Although pins are often made from a solid piece of wood, smaller pieces can be laminated to form a billet. To do this, the small pieces are set aside to be glued edge-to-edge with other narrow pieces and thus form a panel that will become one ply of the laminated billet. Several panels (some may be solid pieces) are carefully faced and glued together to form the square billet. Resin-type adhesives form a hard, durable bond.

The glued billets are processed through two turning operations. The *rough turning,* shown in Fig. 5, quickly

16

shapes the rough billet so it is slightly oversize. A *finish turning* follows this to ensure a smooth completed pin of the exact size required.

Following this, the pins are sprayed with several coats of white lacquer and labeled with the trade mark of the producer. Note the special mask, Fig. 6, used for the darker color. The finished pins are then weighed and sorted so that matched sets, made up of ten pins, have equal weights.

Tennis Rackets

One of the earliest sporting goods products to be laminated was the tennis racket frame. In this particular development, as in many others, it was the shortage of good raw materials which encouraged experimentation with new and better methods of production.

Early research by specialized sporting goods manufacturers developed rigid standards for materials to be used in the construction of the racket. They found that second-growth mountain ash was the best wood available for the solid, steam-bent racket. However, the quantity of this wood was not adequate to supply the increasing demands.

This shortage of stock prompted engineering developments which resulted in discarding the steam bending method in favor of wood laminating for practically all racket frames. This new process consisted of bonding several thin strips of ash together about a form to produce the main portion of the racket.

The thin strips of ash are 64 inches long and are carefully selected for proper grain structure. This is an important step for the strength and weight characteristics of the racket are critical. Each strip of ash is sent through a glue coating machine which applies an even, measured layer of adhesive. The six or more strips are then assembled and placed in the bending machine which, by the use of hydraulic pressure, forces the strips into the basic shape of the racket. Because of the curvature, the outer strip appears to be 1½ inches shorter than the inner strip. A clamp is locked over the strips so that they will retain the correct shape and the entire unit is placed in a kiln. Here the controlled heat and humidity cure the glue.

When cured, the unit is taken from the kiln and the clamps removed. From this point, the frame is sent through the necessary woodworking processes where it is trimmed, fitted with a handle, drilled for string holes, and then finished appropriately. Fig. 7 is an enlarged view of a completed racket frame showing the laminated strips and adjacent glue lines.

Fig. 7 Laminated Racket Frame

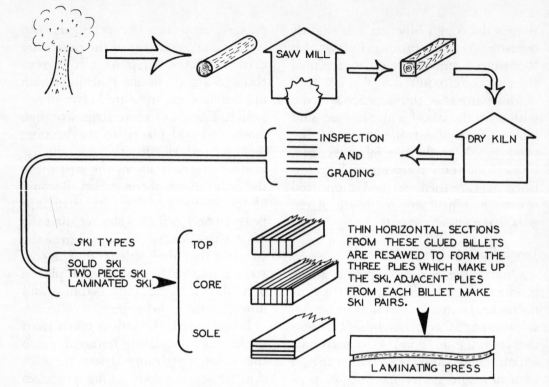

Fig. 8. Production Sequence of a Laminated Ski

Skis

The production of laminated hickory skis presents some interesting and unusual manufacturing problems. Each pair must be closely matched in such characteristics as weight, shape, and flexibility.

Although there are a variety of production methods, one rather characteristic procedure is described in the following paragraphs.

Each ski is made up of three main layers: the top, the core, and the sole. Each ski *top* is cut from a billet made of five plies of selected hickory across its width. The *core* is cut from a similar billet made of seven plies. The *sole* of the ski is solid, flat-grain hickory cut from choice wood. This arrangement staggers the joints and puts the main stresses on the solid stock.

The billets, from which the three main layers are cut, are assembled under rigidly controlled conditions. Tests applied to the glue joints, after they have set properly, must reveal wood failure rather than joint failure. Even the slightest delamination, once the ski has been put into service, would quickly render it useless.

After each billet has cured, the ski layers are cut from across the plies by a power band saw which has been specially fitted for this use. Each layer, as it is taken from the saw, is carefully stacked next to the one cut on the previous pass through the machine. When the operation is finished, these layers are in the same position as they were when the piece was solid.

In the assembly of the skis, much care is taken to be sure that the top

18

layer of each ski in a pair is made from adjacent layers of the billet. This is also true of the other two layers. This is done to make certain that the pair are as nearly alike as possible.

Waterproof resin glue is applied to each layer of the laminate just prior to placing them in special ski presses. These heated presses force the three layers together, shape the tip and the tail, and provide exactly the correct curing temperature to make a permanent waterproof bond. Fig. 8 illustrates graphically the sequence of these operations.

Other manufacturers produce a laminated ski by assembling multiple layers of marine plywood in combination with aluminum, steel, and phenolic resin. Fig. 9 is a photo of the cross section of this type of ski and adjacent to it is a photo of the tip of the finished ski. Note that edgegrain plywood forms a core to which the other materials are attached.

Still other manufacturers use the laminating process only at the curved tip end of the ski. The ski is shaped from solid wood and a saw kerf is cut into the edge of the ski at the tip end. This reduces the thickness of the wood and the bending of this thinner section is accomplished with much less difficulty than with stock of full thickness. In the gluing and bending process, a thin piece of wood is inserted into the kerf so as to maintain the overall thickness of the ski. Wood of this sort, less than $1/4''$ in thickness, is generally called veneer.

CROSS SECTION ENLARGED

Fig. 9. Ski Laminated from Several Materials: 1) Black Phenolic Plastic, 2) Aircraft Aluminum, 3) Steel Edges, All Bonded to Laminated Edgegrain Plywood with Hollow Center (Northland)

Bow Staves

Centuries ago, the Orientals discovered that a superb bow for archery could be made by combining three different basic materials: animal sinew, wood, and horn. The shredded animal sinew, laid in a specialized glue, formed the *back*. A thin strip of *wood interliner* separated the back from the *belly* which was made of horn. This skillfully assembled weapon is still regarded by many as perfection in the bowmaker's art. From these craftsmen came the modern concept of a bow

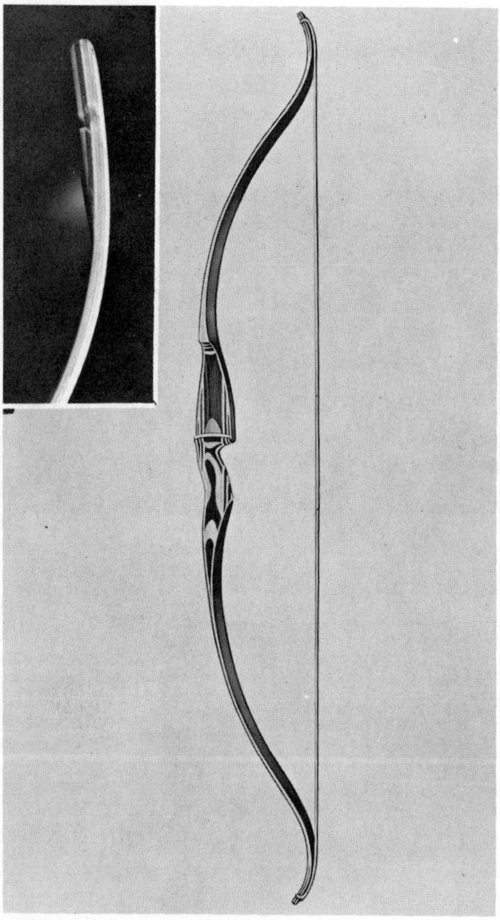

Fig. 10. Laminated Bows — Inset Shows a Reflexed Bow (Pearson)

stave laminated from more than one kind of wood.

Laminating is used for two different purposes in the construction of a bow, reflexing and backing.

Reflexing is the process of bending curved tips or ends on the bow to give it a more graceful and attractive appearance. Straight grain laminating is a practical method of building up this curvature. The inset of Fig. 10 pictures a laminated reflexed bow.

Backing, an exacting process, modifies the characteristics of a bow by increasing its life, adding to its range, and improving its shooting qualities. This is accomplished by gluing a thin strip of wood (or other material) to the back (convex side) of the bow. Frequently hickory, ash, elm, or lemonwood is used. These woods are tough, resilient, straight grained, and have good characteristics of elasticity. The process of backing has been much improved in recent years by the development of new types of glues which are capable of making a glue joint actually stronger than the wood itself. See Fig. 10.

The function which the backing serves can be understood by visualizing the effect of bending a solid piece of wood such as a bow. As tension is applied by pulling on the string, the fibers of wood on the outside of the curve must have just enough elasticity to stretch to this new shape with the proper *tension*. At the same time, the fibers of wood on the inside must properly *compress* to accommodate the shorter position. Woods vary considerably in their characteristics of tension and compression. By combining a wood which stretches well with one which

Fig. 11. Laminated Diving Boards in
Clamps for Gluing (Smith)

compresses well, a better stave results.
A frequent combination is a *hickory
back* and a *lemonwood belly*. A color-
ful wood such a *amaranth* is sometimes
used between these to make a *three-
piece stave*.

Diving Boards

Many wood diving boards currently
being manufactured in the United
States are made from Douglas fir.
This wood is sufficiently flexible and
yet is resilient enough to withstand the
repeated bending that is required of
a diving board. These boards normally
range from twelve to sixteen feet in
length and taper from a thickness of
three inches at the base to one and
one-half inches at the tip. Considering
that these boards must be twenty
inches wide and meet the above quali-
fications, it is understandable that

manufacturers experience difficulty in
the selection of suitable raw material.
This has encouraged many diving
board companies to produce a laminated board.

By careful selection of stock, it is
possible to combine pieces of wood
with exactly the right grain structure
to produce a diving board with super-
ior performance characteristics. Each
of the twelve or more laminated sections runs the full length of the board.
They are bonded together with waterproof glue and further reinforced with
through bolts.

Fig. 11 is a photo of diving boards
set in clamps for the glue curing process. Note that two boards are clamped
with a single set of heavy draw bolts
and blocks. Fig. 12 shows the diving
boards after they have been removed
from the gluing clamps, planed smooth
and trimmed to accurate dimensions.
Following this, a protective finish will
be applied, the board suitably pack-
aged, and then shipped to a pool for
installation.

Fig. 12. Laminated Diving Boards Cut to
Dimension and Stored Prior to Finishing (Smith)

Fig. 13. Steps in Producing Laminated Golf Club Heads (Wilson)

Golf Club Heads

Another laminating process is used extensively in the manufacture of the wood heads for golf clubs. These so-called "woods" are produced by laminating many layers of maple veneer into a basic "V" shape from which the finished head can be shaped. Although this is basically a laminating process, a few crossbands of veneer produce greater strength across the grain.

Fig. 13 shows the basic steps in producing this portion of the wood. At the extreme left is the stock of maple veneer from which the billet will be made. Next, the billet is shown following its removal from the high pressure gluing clamps.

After the billet is roughly shaped by sawing, it is mounted in an automatic lathe to produce the basic shape of the head shown on the extreme right. Fitting the shaft, weighting the head, attaching a sole plate, and facing are but a few of the many finishing processes that produce the club shown in Fig. 14.

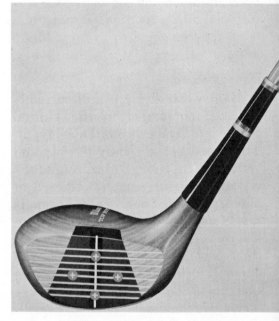

Fig. 14. Finished Golf Club Head (Wilson)

22

Furniture

Another fascinating application of wood laminates is in the furniture industry. Certain contemporary pieces are particularly suitable for construction by the wood laminating method in combination with such other materials as molded plywood, solid wood, fabric, fiber glass, and plastic.

The methods for bonding these laminates have been perfected to the point where the glue line between each layer of veneer is so fine that it is scarcely noticeable. Also, modern glues are of such quality that the veneers will not delaminate under any normal use.

These two factors plus the economy that results from using lower grades of wood and the current emphasis on functional design have encouraged a number of furniture industries to produce a line of wood laminated products.

Chairs

Some of the newer chair styles which have been developed are based upon the practical application of wood laminating. Notable in this group are the Eames chair, Fig. 15, produced by the Herman Miller Company and the Joe Adkinson side chair, Fig. 16, produced by Thonet Industries.

These chairs use a molded plywood for the seat and back. The structural members, however, are laminated. Note that the back support and legs are so shaped that they could not be suitably fashioned from solid wood. Laminated sections produce the desired grace and the strength required by such a structural member.

Fig. 15. Eames Chair (Miller)

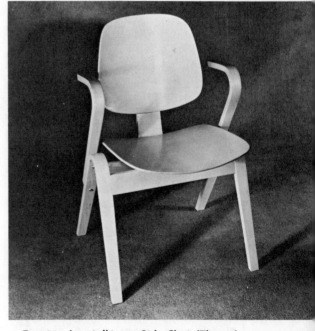

Fig. 16. Joe Adkinson Side Chair (Thonet)

23

Grand Pianos

One of the oldest, well known applications of wood laminating with hard woods is in the piano trade. As early as 1860, the Steinway Company was producing rims for the grand piano in this manner. The process is essentially unchanged today with the exception of a few mechanical improvements in the clamping method and the use of more durable glues.

Each piano style, which requires a variation in the rim shape, necessitates the construction of a permanent form about which that particular rim can be glued. The forms are made of heavy wood sections bolted and glued together. The finished form is mounted on legs for a convenient work height. Clamps are supported from steel pins which are anchored to the form by holes bored at intervals near the edge. The pins permit the clamps to hinge so that they may be properly positioned when clamping pressure is required.

Cauls, which distribute the clamp pressure, are made to fit each form. These are glued from several layers of hardwood veneer in exactly the same manner that the piano rim is formed. Once these have been properly fitted, round steel plates are inserted in the caul at points where the clamps would produce an abnormal amount of wear.

The actual manufacture of a piano rim is comparatively simple once the form and caul have been completed. Selected strips of veneer are end joined so that each layer will be continuous from one end of the rim to the other. Generally, choice hardwood such as mahogany or walnut are used for the outside faces with some less desirable veneer, such as poplar, on the five inner layers. No provision is made for cross-banding. Each piece of veneer is sent through the glue spreading machine for an even coating of adhesive and the stack is then shaped about the form.

Certain precautions must be taken to prevent excess glue from bonding the outside veneers to the wood form and caul. In some cases, thin sheets of metal are inserted next to the caul and form and in others, a generous coating of wax is applied. The unit is allowed to cure at room temperature.

After removal from the press, an additional laminated member is fitted into place on its inner surface. This is

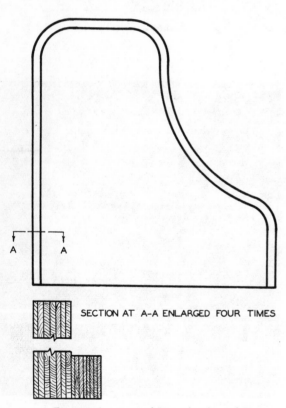

SECTION AT A-A ENLARGED FOUR TIMES

Fig. 17. Laminated Rim of a Grand Piano

24

made of eight layers of hard maple of about one-half the width of the outer rim. Fig. 17 shows the position of this reinforcing rim and the general design of the rim.

After the two laminates which make up the total rim have been assembled, the excess glue is removed and the rim is cut to shape. This particular piece is then ready for assembly with more than five thousand other parts which make a finished piano.

Boat Building

Currently, many boat builders in the United States are using the laminating process to fabricate keels, stems, and ribs. Several companies that manufacture pleasure boats in the thirty-foot to sixty-foot range fabricate boats on a one-piece laminated keel and stem. This unit may be assembled from a dozen or more pieces of wood which may be pre-shaped so that excessive hand work on the bulky finished unit may be eliminated. Other portions of these craft such as ribs, deck carlings (supports), and deck house edges may be made by using this same laminating method.

At least one builder of kit boats is producing a lap strake boat kit which is assembled with a laminated stem and laminated ribs. This enables the inexperienced boat builder to construct a rib-type boat without the usual problems of steam bending ribs and the risk of a hull having irregular contours. Fig. 18 shows a commercial laminating press in which a marine laminate is being glued.

Another interesting development in wood laminating for marine use was in the construction of wooden mine sweepers for the Navy. During the fighting in Korea, the enemy made extensive use of magnetic mines to damage coastal shipping. These mines are set off by the magnetic influence of a steel-hulled ship passing in the vicinity. One counter weapon was the wood-hulled vessel which presumably would have little or no magnetic field about it. A number of these hulls were built and because of their comparatively large size, many laminated wood structural members were required. Fig. 19 shows the skeg (afterpart of keel) for one of the ships being finished in a New Orleans plant. This skeg contains more than 200 individual pieces of selected wood adhered with waterproof glue.

Fig. 18. Commercial Laminating Press (Taft)

Fig. 19. Laminated Skeg
for Marine Use (Higgins)

Fig. 20. Clamping a Laminated Rib for
a Ship (Higgins)

Fig. 21. Laminated Rib and
Keel Assembly (Higgins)

Fig. 22. Stern View of the Laminated
Structural Members in a Ship Hull (Higgins)

The ribs for these vessels were also laminated from strips of oak bent and glued on steel jigs. Fig 20 shows the process of tightening a few of the many clamps. The speed demanded in this operation required that nearly 100 workers be on hand to assemble a single rib. Air-operated impact wrenches, or "nut runners," were used to apply the proper torque to each clamp. In some cases a fire-hose clamping system was used to maintain a continuous pressure of approximately one hundred fifty pounds per square inch on the entire laminated assembly.

The keel and rib skeleton assembly are shown in Fig. 21 prior to the application of external planking. Fig. 22 is a stern view of the same ship. The military forces regarded this vessel as a successful one. Many of this type were built by coastal ship building contractors throughout the United States.

Structural Laminates

Perhaps no other phase of wood laminating is as well known as the structural laminates that are being used extensively for rafters in large buildings. Their graceful, functional lines have made them favored structural members in churches, schools, swimming pools, farm buildings, factories, and gymnasiums.

Most manufacturers of laminated beams and rafters fabricate them from soft woods with a water-resistant adhesive. Woods such as Douglas fir, yellow pine, and spruce are commonly used. The fabrication of each unit is carried out in the factory. The finished rafters or beams are delivered to the job site ready for erection.

In many cases the finished laminate is completely wrapped in waterproof paper so that it will be protected from exposure to the weather prior to its installation in the building.

The production of laminated rafters involves many of the same problems described in relation to other laminating methods. One of the first requirements is adequate space to assemble these large units. The gluing floor is ordinarily fitted with movable brackets which, when adjusted, make up the form upon which the individual rafters are glued. Retaining clamps attached to these brackets hold the laminations in their proper position.

The gluing and assembly room of a rafter laminating plant is shown in Fig. 23. The movable brackets which are set to determine the shape of the rafters are the vertical members that appear behind the rafters in clamps. Notice that two rafters are clamped side by side. In this way, one bolt per clamp provides pressure on each rafter at that particular location.

Lumber for the rafters is carefully selected and, if necessary, edge-joined to produce stock of adequate width. Next, these pieces are end-joined by using a scarf joint to make laminations of sufficient length to reach from one end of the rafter to the other. The joint normally used for this purpose is called a hooked-scarf joint. Fig. 24 shows this joint as it appears on the edge of a laminated rafter. The "hook" retains the joint in position while it is being clamped after gluing. Rafters as long as those shown in Fig. 25 have several such joints in each ply.

When this has been completed, each lamination is checked for proper thick-

Fig. 23. Gluing and Clamping Rafters (Rilco)

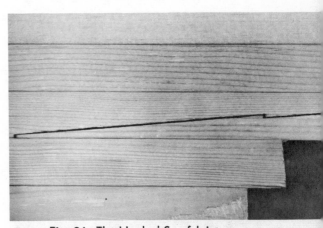

Fig. 24. The Hooked-Scarf Joint

Fig. 25. Laminated Rafters Used to Span a 76 Foot Gymnasium (Rilco)

ness and made ready for the application of glue. Once the adhesive has been applied, the layers are bent around the form and securely clamped into place to produce a strong joint with a thin glue line. Some manufacturers apply heat to the assembly to speed the process; but because of the bulkiness of the rafter, this is sometimes a rather difficult procedure.

When the glue is cured, the rafter is removed from the clamps, cleaned of excess glue, trimmed to proper dimensions, and made ready for delivery to the building site.

A number of applications of structural laminates are shown in Figs. 26 to 29.

Fig. 27. Laminated Columns and Beams Supporting the Roof of a Cafe (Rilco)

Fig. 28. Laminated Flat Wood Beams for Home Construction (Rilco)

Fig. 26. Laminated Arches in a Church (Rilco)

Fig. 29. Erecting Laminated Rafters for a Barn (Rilco)

CHAPTER 2

MATERIALS FOR WOOD LAMINATING

During the past thirty years there have been extensive changes in the glue industry. Perhaps the most outstanding development in this period was the production of waterproof and water-resistant glues. In fact, it was this development that made it possible to produce many of the laminated wood materials described in the previous chapter.

Glues for woodworking that were available before 1930 were made from natural materials. Many of these were excellent adhesives and several of them are marketed in large quantities to this date. Since then chemists have compounded many new synthetic adhesives. This suggests a logical division of the kinds of glues: *natural* and *synthetic*.

Natural Glues

There are two common glues, usable for wood laminating, which come from natural sources. These are *hot animal* or *hide glue,* and *casein glue*, derived from milk.

Hot Animal Glue

Animal glue is made from the gelatin material available from animal bone and hides. It is one of the oldest adhesives used by the woodworking trade and is still valued for its strength and for the nearly invisible glue line which it makes.

However, for several reasons it has limited usefulness in laminating. Since it must be heated prior to being applied to the surfaces to be glued, it will set rapidly. This may be a disadvantage in laminating because the adhesive must be applied to all surfaces before the assembly can be clamped. Accordingly, the glue applied first may set before pressure can be applied to the joint, resulting in a poor glue joint.

A second disadvantage of animal glue for wood laminating is its lack of moisture resistance. Exposure to moisture tends to weaken the completed assembly and eventually would cause delamination.

Thus in wood laminating, hot animal glue could be used on smaller pieces which have a short assembly time, and which will not be exposed to moisture. Its rapid setting may make it useful when speed is a factor.

Casein Glue

This was the first water-resistant glue. Casein glue is made from the curd of cows milk and is sold as a powder.

It is normally mixed with the correct amount of water just a few minutes before it is applied to the wood surface. The clamping pressures are somewhat lower than those required for most of the synthetic glues. In experimental work this may be a decided advantage.

Casein glue will react with some kinds of wood which contain acid and thus produce a dark glue line. For this reason it is recommended that a test glue joint be made with samples of any wood to be used with casein glue.

It should be noted that there are *two classes* of glues for withstanding moisture. *Water-resistant,* implies that the glue will withstand *limited exposure* to moisture. *Waterproof* glues however, will withstand *continuous exposure* to high humidity and such abuse as repeated soaking in boiling water without failure at the glue line.

Casein glue falls into the first class and as such is sufficiently resistant to moisture to be used for the assembly of protected structural members in buildings. Its low cost and comparative ease of application are advantages that are not overlooked by manufacturers of laminated products.

In the gluing industry the term *open time* refers to the permissible delay between the application of the glue to the wood surface and the completion of clamping. Casein glue has an open time which is extensive enough for large industrial assemblies and limited experimental work.

Because of its low cost, easy application. moisture resistance, long open time, and low clamping pressure, it is a very satisfactory glue for experimental laminating.

Synthetic Resin Glues

In contrast to the natural glues there now exists a wide variety of *man-made adhesives.* These have been developed primarily during the last twenty-five years and for some uses have advantages over natural glues. Although a variety of these synthetics is now produced, just a few of them are available to the small consumer and non-commercial user. They are generally referred to as *synthetic resin glues.*

The synthetic resin family of glues was developed in the early years of World War II as a result of a program to find better water-resistant glues. The synthetic adhesives now available can be grouped into two classifications. First, *thermosetting* glues which harden permanently at room temperature as a result of *chemical action.* Second, the *thermoplastic* resins, which are emulsions such as *white polyvinyl glue.* These harden by the *loss of water* and may be resoftened by exposing them to high temperatures. While polyvinyl glue is convenient to use, it has low resistance to high stresses, heat, and moisture.

From the thermo-setting group there are four basic resins. However, only two of them are marketed on a retail basis and accordingly they are described in the following paragraphs.

Urea-Resin Glue

Urea-resin, sometimes called *plastic resin,* is the most popular of the powdered synthetic glues. It is normally sold in dry form and is available in small quantities. It has a long shelf life and may be mixed with water just prior to using. It produces a nearly colorless joint and has good strength characteristics with moderate gluing pressures. This adhesive has good resistance to cold water and humidity. Permissible open time is normally long enough so that complicated gluing jobs may be assembled with care prior to the application of pressure.

Like the other synthetic resin glues, the rate at which urea resin sets is dependent upon the temperature. In general, the higher the temperature, the shorter the curing time. Some industrial concerns make use of this characteristic to reduce the time which an assembly must remain in the clamps. By placing the glued materials in a heated curing room, the urea resin glue matures to maximum strength in a very short time. This makes possible a much shorter gluing cycle and hence more efficient production.

Resorcinol Resin Glue

Of the many resin type glues that are manufactured, resorcinol resin is one of the few that is considered to be completely *waterproof*. When properly mixed, applied, and cured, it forms a glue joint which will withstand repeated soaking and drying or continuous exposure to weather. For this reason, it is frequently used for the assembly of wooden boats or as the adhesive for laminating boat and ship parts.

This glue is also available in small quantities and is sold in a two-container unit. One container holds a powder and the other a dark brown liquid hardening agent. The two are mixed in proper proportions just prior to using. This, like other resin glues, cures at a rate that is dependent upon the temperature. In general, the higher the temperature the more quickly the glue will harden.

Curing temperatures for this adhesive are in the 70-degree Fahrenheit to 80-degree Fahrenheit range and this makes it suitable for use at normal room temperature. It must not be used where the temperature is below 70°F. Once cured, it will develop a joint having strength equal to that of the wood itself. A disadvantage is its color. It drys a dark brown color which is objectionable under some circumstances.

Glue Curing

The preceding paragraphs have indicated that some varieties of glue will set much more rapidly if they are cured in heated rooms. A number of different methods have been developed for heating glued joints and thus speed up the gluing.

Heated Curing Areas

One of the most practical methods for supplying the necessary temperature to set the glue joint is a *heated curing room*. This is an insulated room in which the air temperature and humidity are rigidly controlled. It is a particularly successful method for curing the glue joints in large laminated sections such as roof trusses and ship keels. Structures of this sort have a large cross-sectional area and adequate curing requires that the piece be exposed to heat until the glue on the innermost joint has reached the proper temperature.

Humidity control must also be maintained in these rooms while the curing operation is going on. By so doing, the wood which is being glued can be maintained at a constant moisture content. A serious change in moisture content during this operation might induce appreciable checking and other undesirable defects.

A modification of the heated curing room is used by some manufacturers who find it impractical or too expensive to construct a separate area for this purpose. They achieve a similar effect by supporting the glued assembly over *coils of steam pipes.* The

Fig. 30. Heat Curing the Glue in a Laminated Assembly — Note Heat Indicator (Higgins)

Fig. 31. Thermocouple for Temperature Indicator in a Laminated Assembly (Higgins)

heat, which radiates from the pipes, is confined to the area by a heavy canvas draped over the glued unit and the steam pipes. Fig. 30 is a photo of a laminate being cured in this manner. This system, of course, lacks the accurate control which is possible in an insulated room. In spite of this, the method is used extensively for large timbers.

In some cases, a *thermocouple* is inserted into one of the glue joints to indicate the exact temperature of a glue joint that is being cured. This is an electrical device which senses temperature and reports to a sensitive instrument. Fig. 31 shows a glued assembly in which a thermocouple has been inserted. The connecting wires lead to a temperature indicating instrument.

Radiant Heat

Electric heaters or heat lamps may be used to produce radiant heat to cure glued assemblies. Although the process has not been particularly successful, it is sometimes used for small units and for setting scarf joints prior to laminating.

The primary disadvantage of this heating method is the lack of humidity control. The radiant heat tends to reduce the moisture content of the lumber and in so doing causes checking or other defects. These may impair the strength of the glue joint.

High-Frequency Heating

A recent development for applying heat to a glue joint is known as high-frequency heating. Although this principle of heating has been known for many years, it has been developed essentially since World War II. In design, this equipment resembles a short-wave radio transmitter. However, instead of using an antenna to radiate the energy into space; the high-frequency unit is capable of directing its output either into the wood surrounding the glue joint or into the glue itself. The high-frequency energy causes molecular agitation of the wood or glue and this in turn causes heat.

A distinct advantage of this method is the characteristic of rapid, uniform heating. When this unit is adjusted to penetrate to the glue line, curing takes place almost immediately. This is valuable where speed in production and assembly time are critical factors.

Fig. 32 is a photograph of a high-frequency heating unit designed for use in edge-gluing lumber. The machine is so constructed that stock is automatically positioned and clamped during the curing cycle of a few seconds. Although this unit is complete in itself, others are designed so that the generating unit is mounted in a console and suitable leads carry the radio-frequency energy to the point of application. Such arrangements are sometimes used with large screw presses or with portable curing guns which energize confined areas.

Heating Blanket

A recent development in devices for applying heat to a glued laminated assembly is an electric blanket. It consists of a conductive rubber heating element vulcanized between two layers of flexible, insulating rubber. This pad is about one-tenth of an inch in thickness and is placed next to each outside surface of the laminate during the time it is in the press.

Fig. 32. Electronic Gluing Machine (Reeves)

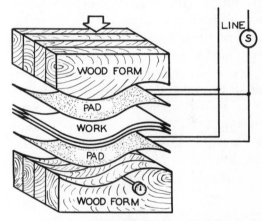

Fig. 33. Heating Pads Being Used to Cure Glue

When the unit has been clamped, heat is turned on, and the pads warm the surrounding wood.

Temperatures of approximately 200°F can be attained in a matter of ten minutes. The thickness of the laminate is the critical item in determining how long the assembly must be exposed to that temperature. Fig. 33 is a simplified sketch of a laminating press set up to make use of the heating pads. Note the thermometer which is inserted near the glue line. This will make it possible to check the internal temperature frequently and eliminate the likelihood of overheating.

Woods for Laminating

A study of laminated products reveals that nearly every available specie of wood has been laminated. In general, the structural laminating industries have used varieties of *softwoods*. The furniture, sporting goods, and marine trade make use of *hardwoods*. This is not a fixed rule for there are many exceptions.

Softwoods

Because of specific demands for structural laminates, the industry has established standards for lumber. In general, the selection corresponds to standard grading procedures since defects in an individual piece of wood tend to weaken the entire assembly once it is laminated. Thus, it is important to eliminate as many of the defects as possible. However, any defects are limited to a single layer and are thus less likely to affect strength.

The structural laminating industry is currently using large quantities of *Douglas fir* and *southern pine*. To lesser extent, *west coast hemlock* and *white fir* are being used.

Hardwoods

Of the hardwoods, *birch* is one of the most popular for general laminating. It is close grained, relatively economical, available in quantity, attractive, and it bends well. *Mahogany* is popular for marine laminates. *Walnut, cherry, mahogany,* and *maple* are frequently used for fine furniture. *Poplar* is sometimes used on unexposed interior layers of bent laminations for pianos and furniture.

Many other hardwoods are laminated to take advantage of their special strength characteristics. Some of these mentioned earlier are: *ash, hickory, hard maple, elm, lemonwood, amaranth, and oak.*

CHAPTER 3

EQUIPMENT FOR WOOD LAMINATING

Industry uses a great variety of *pressure* and *holding devices* for gluing laminated shapes. Each factory and shop creates *forms* and improvises gluing techniques to suit its individual products. The following paragraphs describe the general types of equipment being used for laminating.

Forms Classified

The forms for laminating might be generally classified as either *adjustable* or *fixed*. For example, in the structural laminating field it would be impractical to have a fixed form for each style of rafter that a particular company would make. Thus the arrangement shown in Fig. 23 is used to accommodate a variety of rafter shapes. The "L" shaped brackets may be bolted at any desired location on the gluing floor to establish the contour of a particular rafter.

This general type of form may also be used as a permanent form. A company which has extensive production of a standard laminated shape, may fix a form of this type to the gluing floor and retain the form for repeated use until major changes in design are undertaken.

The common type of *fixed form* is the two-piece fixture consisting of a male and a female die. These are normally used for smaller parts that involve the assembly of veneers. This type lends itself to high production and heated glue curing. Fig. 18 is an example of this type of form.

Another general system for classifying forms used for laminating identifies the form as either *continuous* or *intermittent*. The male and female die would be classified as continuous. The "L" shaped brackets for laminating rafters are an intermittent type of form.

The suitability of one of these two types depends primarily upon the thickness of the individual layers which make up the laminate. Thin layers of veneer are incapable of transmitting gluing pressure to either side of an applied clamp. Thus, an effective glue joint will not result unless pressure is exerted over the entire area to be glued. In contrast to this, the individual pieces of wood which make up a rafter may be thick enough to transmit clamping pressures for several inches to either side of the clamp.

The selection of one of these two types of forms is a matter of determining whether adequate gluing pressure may be maintained along the entire glue line with spaced clamps, or if pressure must be exerted over the entire surface.

Pressure Devices

A great variety of presses and clamps have been devised for exerting pressure on glued laminated assemblies. Several of these are described in the following paragraphs.

Various Presses

Hydraulic and *screw presses* are often used for end-joining and for exerting pressure on male and female dies in the production of small laminates such as tennis rackets and golf club heads.

The larger laminates, rafters, and keels require an interesting procedure when the available lumber is not wide enough or long enough to meet the requirements of the finished laminate. The lumber is first edge-joined to produce stock of the proper width. Next, these pieces are joined end-to-end by means of a scarf joint. A photograph of this joint is shown in Fig. 24. This makes it possible for each layer of the laminate to be continuous from one end to the other.

The screw press can be used efficiently at this point. Several pairs of pieces to be end-joined may be stacked in a screw press and pressure applied to each joint simultaneously.

The air-operated or hydraulic press is particularly convenient when gluing cycles are short for it enables the operator to control high clamping pressures with little effort. Because of their bulk, these units cannot readily be moved from place to place. This restricts the type of work to which they may be applied. Recently, this type of press has been combined with the high frequency technique for curing glue. This combination produces the high clamping pressures with a very rapid curing cycle and accomplishes the task with a minimum of operator effort.

Retaining Clamps

The general term, *retaining clamps*, refers to the light-weight, screw-type clamp used to hold laminations against a form with enough pressure to produce a satisfactory joint. There are several styles which fall into this general classification. A *standard "C" clamp*, a modification of the *carriage clamp*, and fasteners using *threaded bolts* that protrude from the bending jig are all of this type.

In function, they all serve essentially the same purpose. They are spaced at close intervals on the laminating form to distribute even pressure to the glue lines. Blocking materials, referred to as *cauls*, aid in distributing the pressure.

In actual practice, the clamps are *tightened progressively* from one end of the laminate toward the other or from the middle toward each end. This enables the excess glue to be worked out of the joints and each laminate can adjust itself to the correct length.

On large forms, air or electrically operated *nut runners* are used to reduce the hand labor of this tightening process.

Pressure Indicators

Several methods are used to determine the amount of pressure that is being applied by the clamps. One of the most readily available is the *torque wrench*. This is the device often used in the auto mechanics shop to determine that proper pressure is being applied to certain critical bolts on the auto engine. In the laminating shop, this wrench can be adjusted to tighten all clamping nuts to the same pressure. In this way, the correct tension is applied to the clamp and in turn, adequate pressure is applied to the glue joints upon which the clamp bears.

Another pressure indicating device, which is used for laminating is a *compressometer*. It is a steel cylinder and piston built on the hydraulic principle. A pressure gauge is attached to the cylinder head and the cylinder cavity is filled with glycerine. To indicate clamping pressure, this unit is placed between the clamp and the laminate.

As the clamp is turned down, pressure is transferred to the laminate through the piston and cylinder. In so doing, the piston tends to force the glycerine out of the cylinder cavity and the pressure indicator responds accordingly. Because of the high cost of the compressometer, it is used more as a constant for checking clamping pressures and for experimental work rather than as an indicator for an individual clamp.

Fire-Hose Clamping Method

A clamping system which is used by some commercial wood laminaters is referred to as the *fire-hose clamping method*. Its name is acquired from the use of an inflated fire hose which applies pressure to the glue joints. This is accomplished by placing a collapsed fire hose between the clamping caul and the laminate at the time of assembly. Fig. 34 is a cross section drawing of this arrangement.

One end of the hose is plugged and pressure (water, air, or steam) is applied to the other. The hose then tends to inflate and, in so doing, exerts pressure on the laminate and its glue joints. In most cases, two or more hoses are laid side by side to increase the maximum pressure possible.

This clamping system has some distinct advantages. It applies continuous pressure along the laminate rather than the intermittent pressure provided by clamps. It also makes it possible to hold any desired pressure on the glue joints during the entire curing cycle. This is done by maintaining a constant hose pressure. Under some circum-

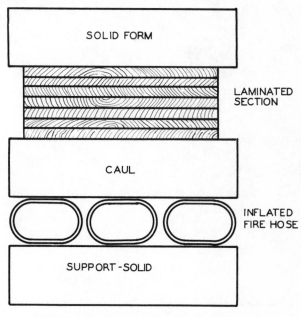

Fig. 34. Fire Hose Laminating Clamp

stances, where external heat is applied to the assembly, a certain amount of wood shrinkage occurs while the glue is curing. Under these conditions, a fixed retaining clamp tends to loosen. However, with the fire-hose method, steady pressure is maintained.

The Nailing Method

Where facilities are limited, nails have been used successfully for applying pressure to the layers of certain glued laminates. Using this method, the first layer is bent around a lami-nating form. Each successive layer is coated with glue and nailed into position on the first layer. This process is repeated until the laminated section is built up to the desired thickness. This procedure seems to offer many possibilities for the individual who may wish to do some laminating for light structural members without heavy and expensive equipment. It would be expected that the quality of the laminate assembled in this manner would not be equal to those clamped with special equipment.

CHAPTER 4

SHOP TECHNIQUES FOR WOOD LAMINATING

Obtaining Veneers and Woods

The veneers and wood required for wood laminating are available from a number of sources depending upon the particular requirements of the project. In most of the wood producing areas of the country there are veneer handling concerns such as veneer mills, plywood factories, or furniture factories. Most of these companies reject a large quantity of veneer as unsuitable for their particular operation and usually destroy this scrap by burning. In many cases this waste product will be available at little or no cost.

If waste veneers are not available, commercial veneers may be purchased or in some instances the experimenter may wish to produce his own veneers. In general, shop produced veneers are less desirable than those commercially available because of the excessive waste in sawing and the tendency for these veneers to vary in thickness. Common thicknesses are $\frac{1}{32}''$, $\frac{1}{27}''$, $\frac{1}{20}''$, and $\frac{1}{16}''$, but others are available.

Selecting Kinds of Wood

Although almost any kind of wood can be laminated, there are certain species that tend to be more suitable than others. In the thin veneers of $\frac{1}{8}''$ and less, the close-grained hardwoods are very satisfactory. Outstanding in this group is *birch*. It is quite readily available, it bends well and produces an attractive finished product.

For larger laminates, the softwood varieties of *pine* and *fir* produce light weight but strong laminated parts.

As with any wood project, be sure the wood selected has the characteristics required for the job. For example, *maple* is fine for interior furniture, but rots readily when exposed to moisture or weathering.

Selecting Veneer Thickness

The *thickness of veneer* is the critical factor in determining the minimum radius about which it may be bent. Other factors which markedly influence this are grain pattern and density of the wood. In selecting the proper thickness of veneer for a particular laminating project, a sample of the veneer may be bent around a radius equal to that of the minimum curvature of the form to be used. If the sample will bend about this radius without breaking, this may be regarded as a satisfactory thickness for the laminating job.

The *moisture content* of the veneer will also modify the bending radius. In general, the higher the moisture content of the veneer the sharper it can be bent without breaking. This is the reason that a glued stack of veneers will bend with less difficulty than will the same stack of veneers dry. The moisture in the glue is rapidly absorbed by the veneers and as a result the thin wood becomes more flexible.

It should be noted at this point that it is usually desirable to select the veneer for a particular project on the basis of the *maximum thickness* that will bend about the minimum radius. This is suggested for two reasons. *First,* the fewer the laminations the less difficulty and time delay there will be in gluing and clamping the stack. *Secondly,* less distortion and warping is usually experienced with pieces formed of thicker and fewer veneers. This is probably due to the fact that thinner pieces of wood absorb a larger quantity of moisture from the glue applied to each surface. Thicker pieces, having fewer glue lines, absorb less of the moisture from the glue.

In some extreme cases where the available veneer is too thick to bend a specific radius, it may be soaked in water, bent about the laminating form and *allowed to dry* in this position. The drying time for this wood may be as much as several weeks, hence this is a very slow procedure and not normally recommended. If the stock is glued prior to adequate drying, a faulty glue joint will most certainly result.

Applying Glue

The application of an adhesive to the veneers is a hand process which needs little explanation. Although there are several methods by which this may be accomplished, one of the most satisfactory is the use of a glue brush. If the mixing proportions are followed for plastic resin or casein glues, the consistency lends itself to easy brushing and uniform distribution. It is generally recommended that both surfaces of the glue joint be coated with adhesive so as to guarantee adequate coverage and thus produce a good bond.

Large veneer areas may also be coated with adhesive by means of a rubber roller or printers' brayer. With this method, a quantity of glue is poured on to the sheet of veneer and then rolled or spread about with the roller. Rolling is much faster than brushing if the pieces of veneer are wide enough to accommodate the roller.

Once the veneers have been coated with glue, they should be stacked together and clamped as quickly as possible.

The actual allowable open time depends upon the kind of glue and the room temperature. Little difficulty in this matter will be experienced if the number of laminations are kept to a minimum and if the forms are well designed to facilitate clamping without delay.

Preparing Forms and Clamps

Perhaps the most critical part in determining the success of a laminated project is the design of the form used to clamp the parts to shape. Each new shape requires a form to suit its particular contours. The following is a selection of forms and clamps which has been found to be most successful for limited usage.

Circular Tension Band Clamps

Perhaps the simplest type of laminating clamp and form is a *commercial tension band clamp* for a circular form. Fig. 35 shows this type of clamp being used to bind a stack of glued veneers around a discarded cast iron flywheel. The center form need not be cast iron but may be wood or other rigid material.

This clamping system does require, however, that the form be *exactly circular* in shape. Any deviation in the shape causes an abrupt change in the pressure applied at that point of change.

Shop-made tension bands of galvanized iron, mild steel, or especially stainless steel may be substituted for the commercial band. In smaller sizes, such devices as the geared type of hose clamp may be substituted for the tension band.

Tension Band Clamps for Curved Form

A shop-made form which produces very satisfactory results in laminating shapes with flat surfaces adjacent to a curve is the tension band and wood form with auxiliary clamps. Figs. 36 and 37 show this type form. In this style of clamp, the *band* produces the necessary gluing pressure on the *curve* while the bolts draw down *cauls* to produce pressure on the *flat surfaces* adjacent to the curve.

The basic part of this form is made from hardwood of adequate thickness to match the width of the laminate to

Fig. 35. Commercial Tension Band Clamp (Adjustable Clamp)

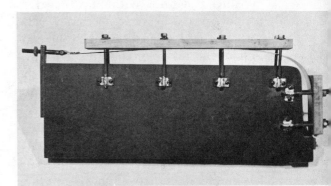

Fig. 36. Tension Band Clamp with Bolted Wood Caul

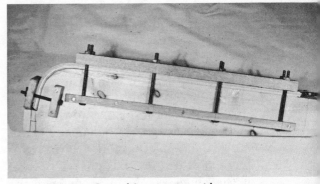

Fig. 37. Curved Lamination with Veneer under Pressure

41

Fig. 38. Bolts for Tension Band Clamps

the pressure resulting from tension on the band.

This tension bolt may be devised in several different ways. Two of the most practical are shown in Fig. 38. In each case a loop is riveted on the free end of the tension band and either a "U" shaped bolt or a "T" shaped bolt is inserted through this loop .

Additional clamps must be provided for the flat areas of the form. These may be drawn down directly over the tension band by using standard bar clamps or by devising a bolted caul for each flat surface.

The clue for good laminating with this type of form is to provide the laminates with adequate pressure uniformly distributed.

If the forms are made of wood, precautions must be taken to assure that the surplus glue does not adhere to the form. This may be done by protecting the form with *waxed paper* or with thin sheets of *polyethylene plastic.* The plastic may be attached to the form with staples and may be reused several times for the gluing and clamping process. Any surplus glue which drys on the plastic will break loose when the laminate is removed. Although waxed paper will also protect the form, it will need to be replaced for each gluing sequence. Also, small quantities of wax from the paper may be transferred to the face veneer and this, if not properly removed, will interfere with the finishing process.

Two-Piece Laminating Form

The two-piece form is made from two pieces of hardwood shaped in a manner of matched male and female dies. This form is somewhat more

be glued. Multiple layers of wood may be glued together with hardboard to produce the thickness necessary. The form should be band sawed to the contour of the inside of the finished laminate and carefully checked to be certain that this edge is true and not crowned.

Tension bands of *stainless steel* have been found to be most suitable. This material has high tensile strength and has no tendency to stain the lighter colored woods, as do some of the more readily available sheet metals. As a substitute, galvanized steel may be used, but it is less suitable because of its soft texture and tendency to kink and stretch.

Tension on the band may be produced by attaching a bolt to the free end of the band and drawing this bolt through a hole in the end of the form. Tightening this bolt when the laminates are in place in the form, produces pressure on the curved portion of the veneers only. The sharper the curve of the form, the greater will be tedious to make than the other types but, if properly made, it will produce a high quality laminate. Figs. 39 and 40 are two-piece laminating forms.

In making such a form, the portion with the concave (hollowed) shape should be made first. Careful layout and sawing is very important. Any final surfacing of this portion of the form may be done on a spindle sander or by hand.

To provide a degree of *resilience*, it is advisable to pad this half of the die with some type of gasket material. This resilience provides for a small amount of variation in the veneer or in the shape of the form. Suitable materials are *rubber* and *cork*. Gasket cork and bulletin board cork are very satisfactory. Cork may be adhered with any of the usual woodworking glues. Contact cement may be required for other materials such as rubber.

The design of the remaining piece of the die may be drawn by locating the first (finished) half above the second half. A sharp pair of dividers is set to the exact thickness of the veneers to be glued and a line scribed by guiding one leg of the dividers against the resilient surface of the completed half of the form. Accuracy is very important in laying out and cutting this part.

The accuracy of the finished form is determined by clamping the proper number of veneers *without* glue. Examination of these veneers under pressure will reveal any areas which will not glue properly and those areas of the form which need adjustment.

With this type of clamping device it is also necessary to *protect the face of the forms from surplus glue* by covering them with plastic film. This is particularly important for the portion covered with resilient material for most glues will adhere to porous surfaces.

Clamping pressure for this type of form can be applied in several different ways. Bar clamps or hand screws may be used to draw the form together, but some type of alignment device must be used to keep the two halves of the form from slipping.

Another rather easily designed clamping method uses machine bolts mounted on either side of the forms

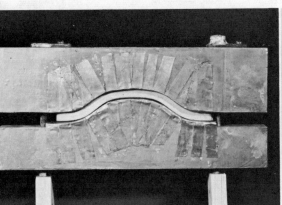

Fig. 39. Two-Piece Laminating Form for a Drawer Pull

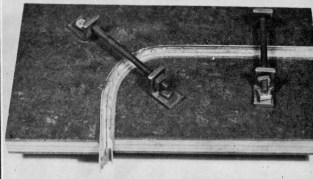

Fig. 40. Two-Piece Laminating Form for a Wall Lamp Bracket

or inserted into holes drilled through the forms. These bolts not only apply pressure to the clamped material but also keep the two halves of the forms in alignment.

In situations where exact clamping pressures are desired, the machine bolts may be drawn up with the aid of a tension or torque wrench. By using this wrench, uniform pressure can be applied to each bolt and to each laminate in duplicate gluing operations.

Fire-Hose Clamp

The fire-hose clamping system makes use of a two-piece form that is designed to accommodate a length of flattened fire hose adjacent to the laminate that is being glued. The assembled veneers are laid in the form next to the flattened fire hose and the form is closed. To apply pressure to the veneers, inflate the hose using either air or hydraulic fluid. Maintain pressure until the glue has set properly.

There are two distinct advantages of this form. The hose, being flexible, tends to conform to the shape of the form and as a result only limited ac-

curacy is required of the pressure part of the form. Secondly, pressure is distributed evenly over the entire surface of the veneers to produce a high quality glue joint.

The construction of this form is very similar to that of the two-piece form. The spacing between the parts of the forms must be adequate, however, to accommodate the flattened fire hose in addition to the glued veneers.

Steel or wood straps may be used to retain the two halves of the form as in Fig. 41. Since these are installed prior to inflating the hose, they may be designed to set into place with limited pressure.

This form, too, needs to be protected with plastic film so that the surfaces will not be damaged by excess glue. Since the fire hose has a fabric cover, it too should be covered with a plastic sleeve. This can be made by wrapping the plastic around the hose and stapling the two edges together.

Either air or hydraulic pressure may be used as shown in Fig. 42. In preparation for this, a suitable fitting must

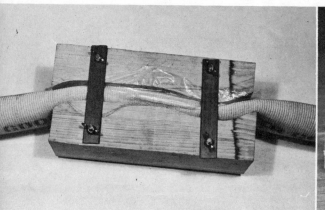

Fig. 41. Fire-Hose Laminating Form
(Goodyear)

Fig. 42. Fire Hose Form Being Used with
Hydraulic Pressure

be inserted into the hose and the ends of the hose clamped together with two blocks of hard wood drawn tight with machine bolts. A valve stem from an automobile inner tube makes a satisfactory connecting fitting.

Since most glues, used in this type of assembly, require gluing pressures in the range of 100 pounds per square inch, the hydraulic or compressed air supply must be capable of supplying pressures that approach this figure. Some compressors or pumps will not produce this much pressure.

Hydraulic pressures are readily obtained by the use of a hand-operated hydraulic pump as shown in Fig. 42. This is a fire-hose form for laminating a compound or "S" shaped curve using a pressure of 125 pounds per square inch.

WARNING: Caution must be used in handling this equipment when air pressures are involved. If the form or its retaining members should break loose under pressure, these parts could *explode* with considerable force. Every precaution should be taken to avoid this possibility. When hydraulic pressure is used, this risk is reduced. The hydraulic fluids are not compressed and thus do not have the stored energy as does the compressed air. Hydraulic fluid is preferred to water as the latter rusts some of the equipment.

The Laminating Sequence

The following description and photos explain the step-by-step procedure to glue a laminated leg using a tension band clamp and a wood form with bolted cauls.

Fig. 43. Cutting Veneers to Length with Tin Snips

1. Cut Veneer to Size

In Fig. 43 birch veneers are being *cut to length* with a pair of sharp tin snips. Veneers, up to approximately $\frac{1}{16}''$, may be cut readily in this manner without splitting or otherwise damaging the veneer.

These particular veneers have been cut to the correct width by using a fine blade on a circular saw and guiding a straight edge of the veneer against the rip fence.

Pieces should be cut oversize so that a smoothing cut can be made on the sides and ends of the finished laminate. Usually pieces are cut $\frac{1}{8}''$ to $\frac{1}{2}''$ wider and several inches longer than the finished size. It may be desirable to mold the laminate double width and later cut it into two pieces.

2. Make a Trial Assembly

After pieces are cut, it is best to make a trial assembly by clamping them without glue. This will show if sizes are correct and adequate allowance was made for bends. It also provides the practice needed to develop the best clamping procedures.

Fig. 44. Applying Glue to Stacked Veneers

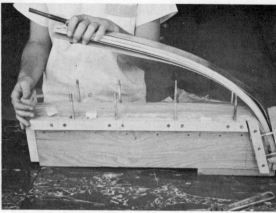

Fig. 45. Bending the Glued Stack of Veneers

3. Stack and Apply Glue

When the proper number of pieces of veneer have been cut, they are stacked for gluing as shown in Fig. 44. In this case, the glue is applied with a brush and each surface is uniformly coated. Note that the pieces of veneer have been stacked together following glue application. This tends to retard the drying time so that the glue does not set prior to clamping.

4. Insert in Form

In Fig. 45 the stack of glued veneers has been inserted into the laminating form. They have been carefully positioned and are being held in place by the lower caul.

5. Tighten Clamps

The "T" bolt of the tension band is inserted into the end block and drawn up as shown in Fig. 46. Then the large caul is positioned on top of the band (Fig. 47), and tightened as shown in Fig. 48. Note that pressure is first applied at one end then applied progressively toward the opposite end. Those bolts nearest the curve are tightened before those nearer the loose end. This allows any bubbles of air

Fig. 46. Drawing the Tension Band

Fig. 47. Positioning the Top Caul

or excess glue to be worked out rather than being trapped. A final check should be made to be certain that all pressures are uniform.

6. Release When Dry

After suitable drying time, the caul bolts and the tension band are released and the rough laminate is removed from the form as shown in Fig. 49. In Fig. 50 a layout is being made on the rough laminate in preparation for sawing. A similar finished leg is shown in the foreground.

Completing Work

When wood laminates are removed from the gluing form, they are normally coated with excess glue and layers are somewhat misaligned. Because of this, truing and finishing are usually required. The exact procedure for doing this will depend upon the shape of the piece and the equipment available. A few of the possible methods are described in the following paragraphs.

CAUTION: The operator doing cutting operations on wood laminates, either with a machine or by hand should *wear goggles.* There is always some possibility of an eye injury resulting from flying particles of glue or chips of veneer.

Cutting to Size

Cutting a laminate to size with one of a variety of saws is a customary way of rough shaping. Within the limits of the machine, a *band saw* may be used for removing excess material on a laminate with a single curve. *The assembly must be fed into the machine so that the surface of the stock adjacent to the cut is resting solidly on*

Fig. 48. Tightening the Top Caul

Fig. 49. Removing the Rough Laminate from the Form

Fig. 50. Making the Layout on the Rough Laminate

the table of the machine at all times. Check this cutting operation carefully to be certain that no risk is involved.

The *portable jig saw* may also be used for this rough cutting operation. The stock is clamped rigidly in a vise or on a bench and the operator cuts along suitable guide lines so as to allow for final sanding. Fig. 51 pictures this operation. Because of the many layers of glue encountered by the saw, blades will tend to dull more rapidly than when used for sawing solid stock. This problem can be overcome by "touching up" the teeth of the saw blade with a saw file.

The *disk sander* equipped with coarse abrasive paper is also a satisfactory machine for roughing down the laminate.

Another tool found useful for this purpose is the *carbide-coated steel saw blade* mounted on a table saw arbor and used in combination with the rip fence. This is a safe and satisfactory cutting system. For best results, the rip fence and the blade should be adjusted to remove small quantities of stock as shown in Fig. 52. It is particularly important in this case for the operator to *wear goggles* as protection against injury from flying chips of wood and hard glue.

Hand Finishing Operations

The usual hand woodworking tools serve well in the final smoothing of the wood laminate once it has been cut to shape. *Scrapers, wood files,* and a variety of *abrasive papers* produce excellent results.

On some laminates, a *plane* might cut satisfactorily. However, laminates are normally assembled without regard to grain direction. Accordingly, some sections of a laminate may plane well and others may splinter and tear out ahead of the cut.

Fig. 51. Cutting Laminate with a Portable Jig Saw (Porter-Cable)

Fig. 52. Cutting Laminate with a Carbide Coated Saw Blade (Skill)

Adding a Protective Finish

All acceptable wood finishing methods are satisfactory for laminated woods. Brushing and spraying lacquers are particularly recommended for furniture and other interior applications. Because of the rapid drying time, it is possible to build attractive lacquer finishes in a short period.

Lacquer may also be applied to the larger laminated parts with the usual spraying equipment. For spray application of stains and lacquer to smaller parts, an air brush will prove to be useful. Because of the lower volume of air and smaller quantity of lacquer expelled by this device, it does not have the tendency to blow the article being finished away from the operator. Fig. 53 is a photo of an air brush being used on narrow parts.

Exterior application of wood laminates demand the usual protective coating of exterior wood finishes. High

Fig. 53. Spraying Finish on a Narrow Surface with an Air Brush (Binks)

grade exterior varnish and outside paints protect the wood and shield the many glue joints from damage resulting from continuous exposure to moisture.

PART II

SELECTED
PROJECTS

This section presents nineteen projects selected with the learner in mind. They vary from simple objects to more complex ones. In each case the laminated portion was selected as a part of the design because it fulfills a functional purpose better than other materials.

Although the drawing describes the project in detail, variations in each of the designs are normally possible. These projects will be suggestive of many others. The beginner will achieve greatest success with the simpler forms, while the more able workers can design their own projects and improvise the necessary forms to produce them.

51

TRIVET

TRIVET

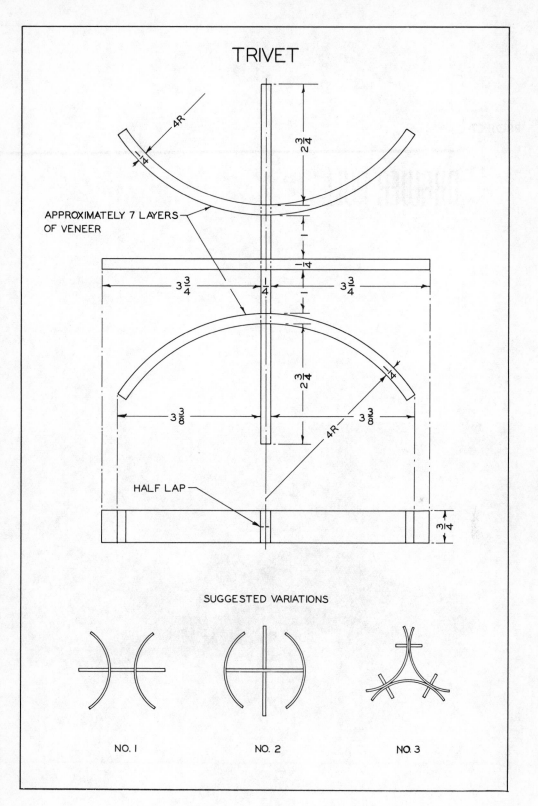

APPROXIMATELY 7 LAYERS OF VENEER

4R

$2\frac{3}{4}$

$\frac{1}{4}$

$3\frac{3}{4}$

$\frac{1}{4}$

$3\frac{3}{4}$

$\frac{1}{4}$

$2\frac{3}{4}$

$3\frac{3}{8}$

$3\frac{3}{8}$

4R

HALF LAP

$\frac{3}{4}$

SUGGESTED VARIATIONS

NO. 1

NO. 2

NO. 3

DRAWER PULL

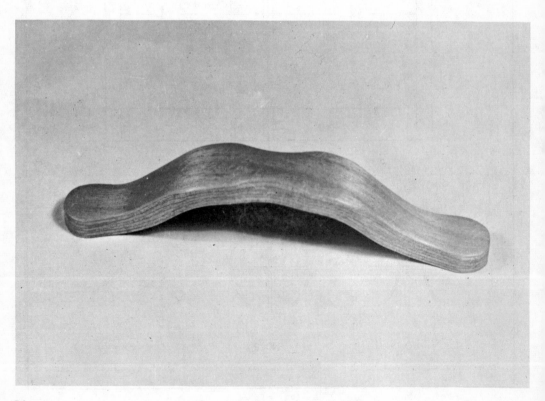

DRAWER PULL

NOTE: DRAWER PULL CONSISTS OF APPROXIMATELY
8 LAYERS OF VENEER.
SECURE PULL TO DRAWER WITH NO. 10 WOOD
SCREWS RD.HD.$\frac{3}{4}$ LG.

PIN-UP LAMP

PIN-UP LAMP

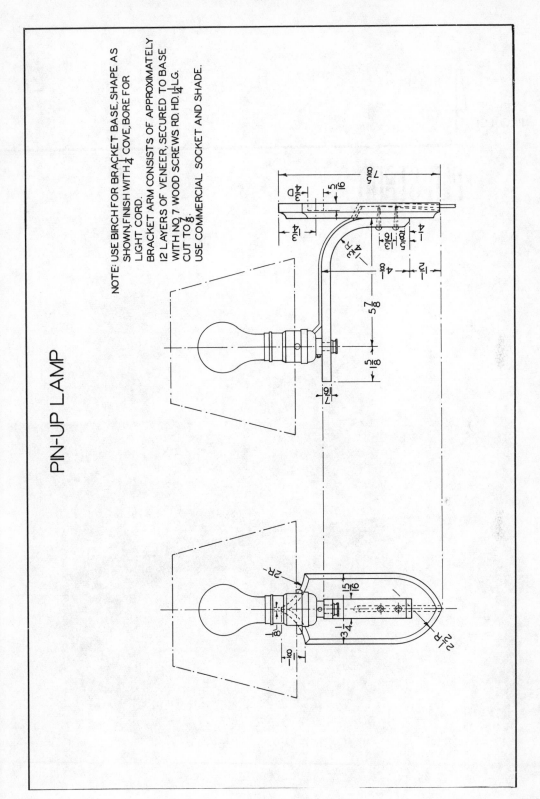

NOTE: USE BIRCH FOR BRACKET BASE, SHAPE AS
SHOWN, FINISH WITH $\frac{1}{4}$ COVE, BORE FOR
LIGHT CORD.
BRACKET ARM CONSISTS OF APPROXIMATELY
12 LAYERS OF VENEER, SECURED TO BASE
WITH NO. 7 WOOD SCREWS RD. HD. $1\frac{1}{4}$ LG.
CUT TO $\frac{7}{8}$.
USE COMMERCIAL SOCKET AND SHADE.

PEN STAND

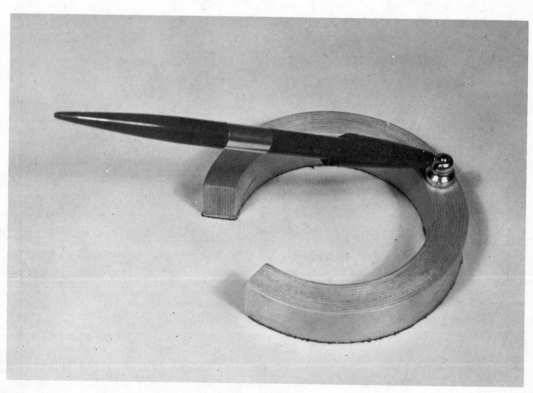

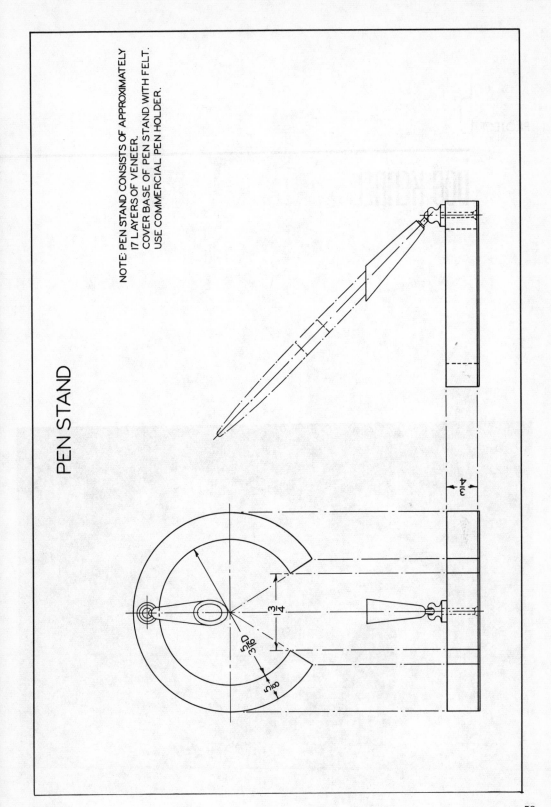

PEN STAND

NOTE: PEN STAND CONSISTS OF APPROXIMATELY
17 LAYERS OF VENEER.
COVER BASE OF PEN STAND WITH FELT.
USE COMMERCIAL PEN HOLDER.

DOG KENNEL

DOG KENNEL

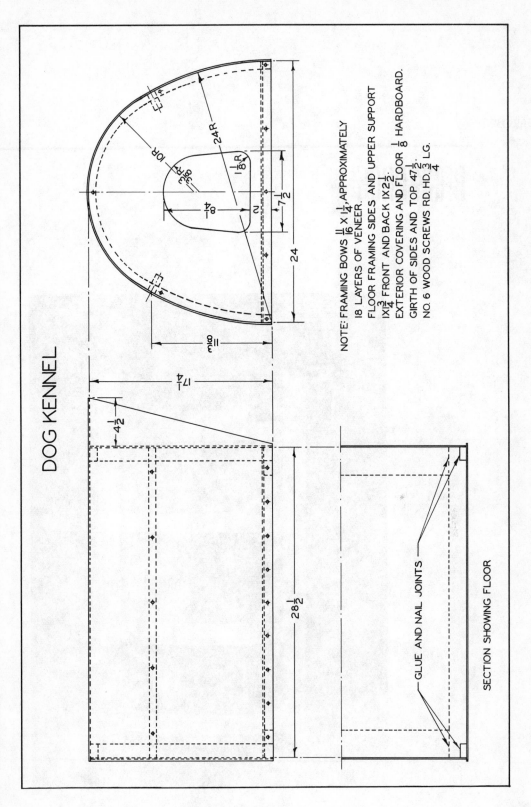

NOTE: FRAMING BOWS $\frac{11}{16} \times 1\frac{1}{4}$, APPROXIMATELY
18 LAYERS OF VENEER.
FLOOR FRAMING SIDES AND UPPER SUPPORT
$1 \times 1\frac{3}{4}$ FRONT AND BACK $1 \times 2\frac{1}{2}$.
EXTERIOR COVERING AND FLOOR $\frac{1}{8}$ HARDBOARD.
GIRTH OF SIDES AND TOP $47\frac{1}{2}$.
NO. 6 WOOD SCREWS RD. HD. $\frac{3}{4}$ LG.

GLUE AND NAIL JOINTS

SECTION SHOWING FLOOR

61

BACK PACK

BACK PACK

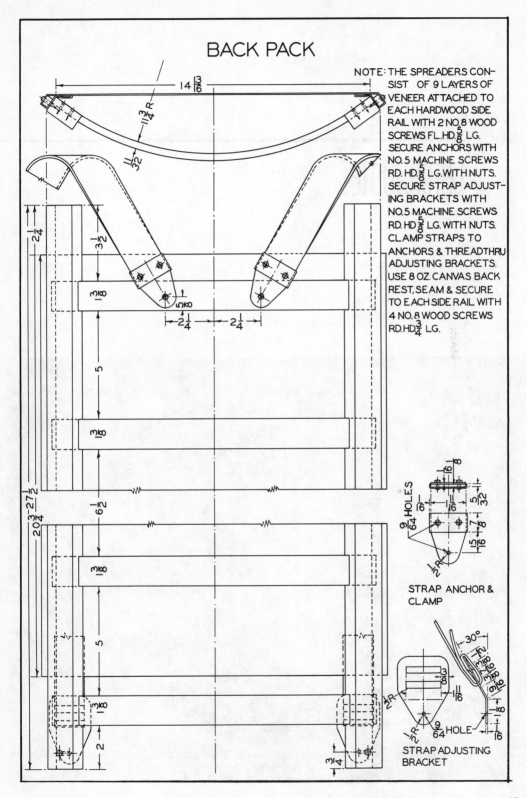

NOTE: THE SPREADERS CONSIST OF 9 LAYERS OF VENEER ATTACHED TO EACH HARDWOOD SIDE RAIL WITH 2 NO. 8 WOOD SCREWS FL. HD. $\frac{5}{8}$ LG. SECURE ANCHORS WITH NO. 5 MACHINE SCREWS RD. HD. $\frac{5}{8}$ LG. WITH NUTS. SECURE STRAP ADJUSTING BRACKETS WITH NO. 5 MACHINE SCREWS RD. HD. $\frac{5}{8}$ LG. WITH NUTS. CLAMP STRAPS TO ANCHORS & THREAD THRU ADJUSTING BRACKETS. USE 8 OZ. CANVAS BACK REST, SEAM & SECURE TO EACH SIDE RAIL WITH 4 NO. 8 WOOD SCREWS RD. HD. $\frac{3}{4}$ LG.

STRAP ANCHOR & CLAMP

STRAP ADJUSTING BRACKET

LANDING NET

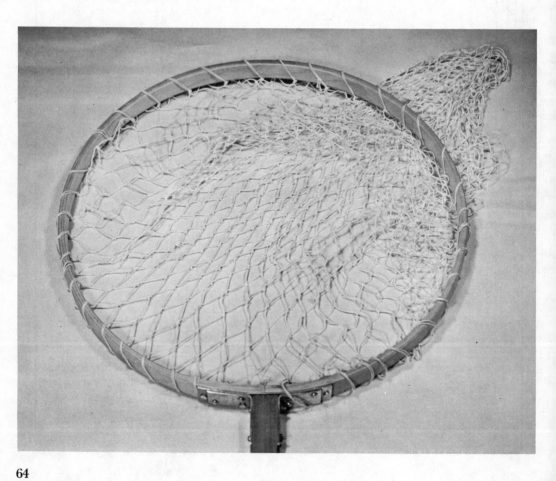

LANDING NET

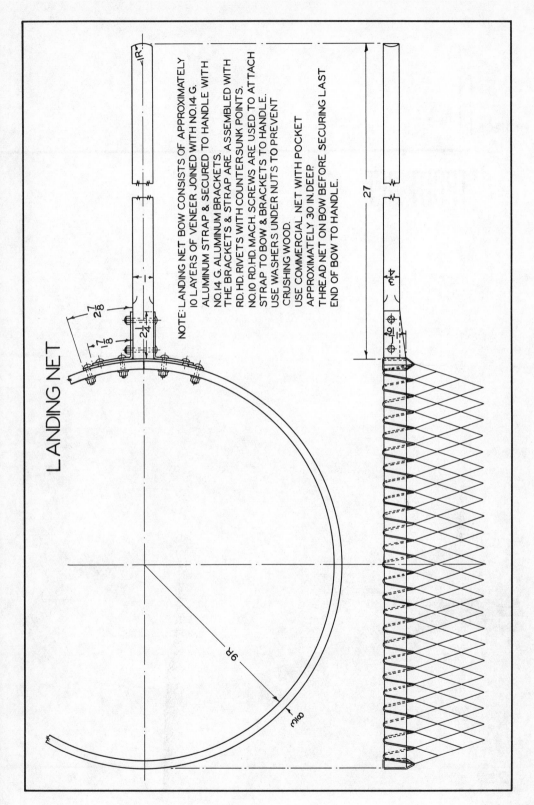

NOTE: LANDING NET BOW CONSISTS OF APPROXIMATELY
10 LAYERS OF VENEER JOINED WITH NO.14 G.
ALUMINUM STRAP & SECURED TO HANDLE WITH
NO.14 G. ALUMINUM BRACKETS.
THE BRACKETS & STRAP ARE ASSEMBLED WITH
RD. HD. RIVETS WITH COUNTERSUNK POINTS.
NO.10 RD.HD. MACH. SCREWS ARE USED TO ATTACH
STRAP TO BOW & BRACKETS TO HANDLE.
USE WASHERS UNDER NUTS TO PREVENT
CRUSHING WOOD.
USE COMMERCIAL NET WITH POCKET
APPROXIMATELY 30 IN.DEEP
THREAD NET ON BOW BEFORE SECURING LAST
END OF BOW TO HANDLE.

TROUT NET

TROUT NET

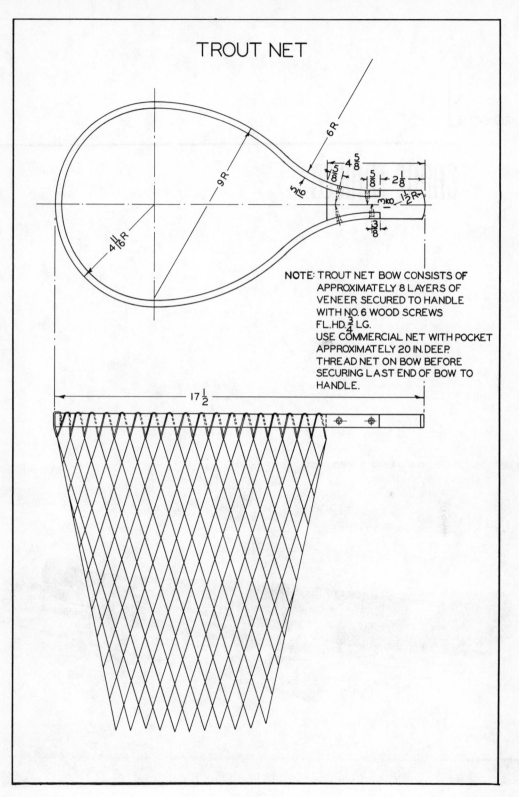

NOTE: TROUT NET BOW CONSISTS OF
APPROXIMATELY 8 LAYERS OF
VENEER SECURED TO HANDLE
WITH NO. 6 WOOD SCREWS
FL. HD. $\frac{3}{4}$ LG.
USE COMMERCIAL NET WITH POCKET
APPROXIMATELY 20 IN. DEEP.
THREAD NET ON BOW BEFORE
SECURING LAST END OF BOW TO
HANDLE.

CANOE TRAILER

CANOE TRAILER

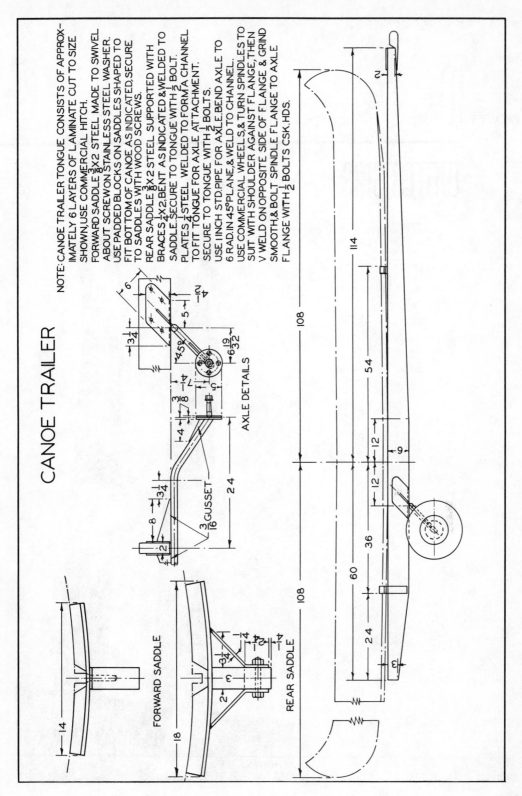

NOTE: CANOE TRAILER TONGUE CONSISTS OF APPROXIMATELY 6 LAYERS OF LAMINATE CUT TO SIZE SHOWN. USE COMMERCIAL HITCH.
FORWARD SADDLE $\frac{3}{8}$X2 STEEL MADE TO SWIVEL ABOUT SCREW ON STAINLESS STEEL WASHER. USE PADDED BLOCKS ON SADDLES SHAPED TO FIT BOTTOM OF CANOE AS INDICATED, SECURE TO SADDLES WITH WOOD SCREWS.
REAR SADDLE $\frac{3}{8}$X2 STEEL SUPPORTED WITH BRACES $\frac{1}{4}$X2, BENT AS INDICATED & WELDED TO SADDLE. SECURE TO TONGUE WITH $\frac{1}{2}$ BOLT.
PLATES $\frac{1}{4}$ STEEL WELDED TO FORM A CHANNEL TO FIT TONGUE FOR AXLE ATTACHMENT. SECURE TO TONGUE WITH $\frac{1}{2}$ BOLTS.
USE INCH STD. PIPE FOR AXLE. BEND AXLE TO 6 RAD. IN 45° PLANE, & WELD TO CHANNEL. USE COMMERCIAL WHEELS, & TURN SPINDLES TO SUIT WITH SHOULDER AGAINST FLANGE, THEN V WELD ON OPPOSITE SIDE OF FLANGE & GRIND SMOOTH & BOLT SPINDLE FLANGE TO AXLE FLANGE WITH $\frac{1}{2}$ BOLTS CSK. HDS.

AXLE DETAILS

FORWARD SADDLE

REAR SADDLE

WATER SKIS

WATER SKIS

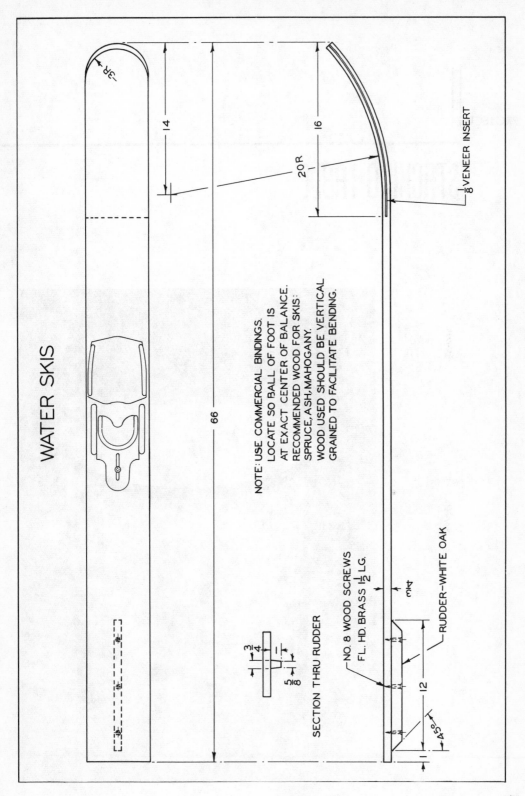

-3R

14

16

20R

$\frac{1}{8}$ VENEER INSERT

66

NOTE: USE COMMERCIAL BINDINGS.
LOCATE SO BALL OF FOOT IS
AT EXACT CENTER OF BALANCE.
RECOMMENDED WOOD FOR SKIS:
SPRUCE, ASH, MAHOGANY.
WOOD USED SHOULD BE VERTICAL
GRAINED TO FACILITATE BENDING.

SECTION THRU RUDDER

$\frac{3}{4}$

$\frac{1}{1}$

$\frac{5}{8}$

NO. 8 WOOD SCREWS
FL. HD. BRASS 1$\frac{1}{2}$ LG.

$\frac{3}{4}$

RUDDER—WHITE OAK

12

45°

1

STACKING TABLE

STACKING TABLE

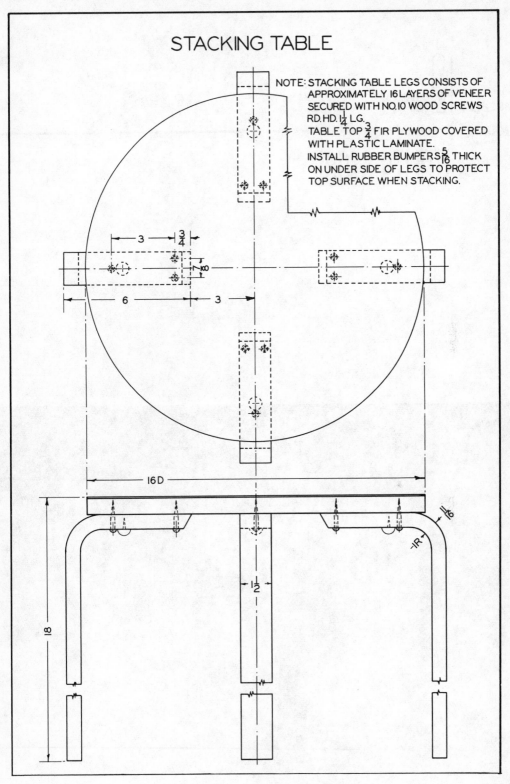

NOTE: STACKING TABLE LEGS CONSISTS OF
APPROXIMATELY 16 LAYERS OF VENEER
SECURED WITH NO. 10 WOOD SCREWS
RD. HD. $1\frac{1}{4}$ LG.
TABLE TOP $\frac{3}{4}$ FIR PLYWOOD COVERED
WITH PLASTIC LAMINATE.
INSTALL RUBBER BUMPERS $\frac{5}{16}$ THICK
ON UNDER SIDE OF LEGS TO PROTECT
TOP SURFACE WHEN STACKING.

UTILITY STOOL

UTILITY STOOL

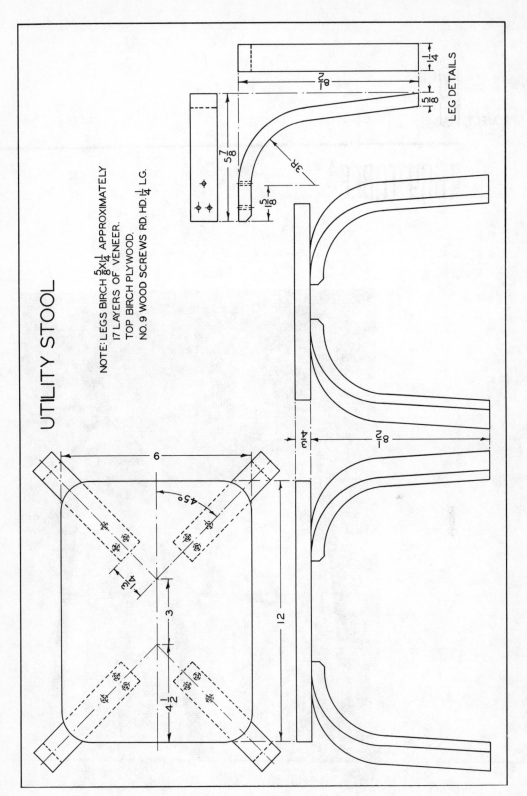

NOTE: LEGS BIRCH $\frac{5}{8}$X$1\frac{1}{4}$ APPROXIMATELY
17 LAYERS OF VENEER.
TOP BIRCH PLYWOOD.
NO. 9 WOOD SCREWS RD. HD. $1\frac{1}{4}$ LG.

LEG DETAILS

TRAY TABLE

TRAY TABLE

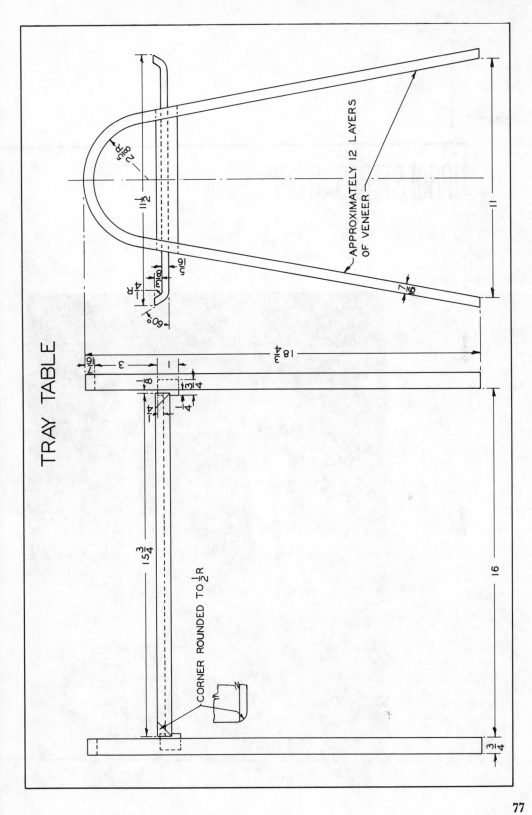

UPHOLSTERED STOOL

UPHOLSTERED STOOL

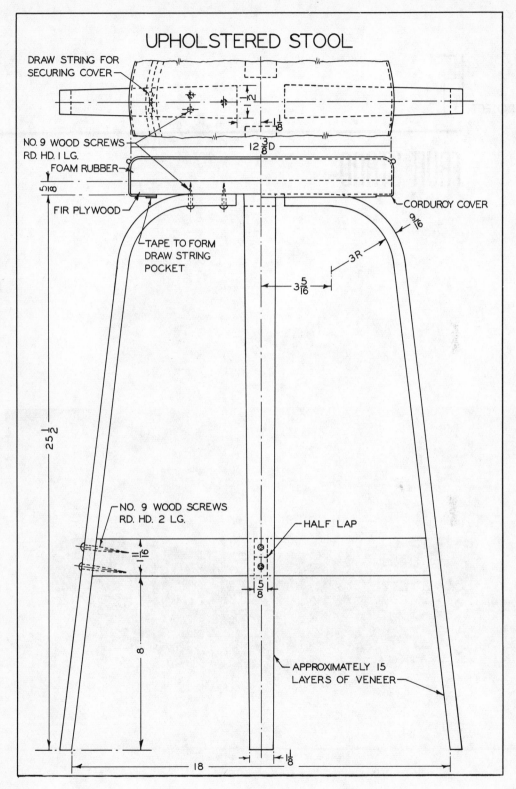

DRAW STRING FOR
SECURING COVER

NO. 9 WOOD SCREWS
RD. HD. I LG.

FOAM RUBBER

FIR PLYWOOD

TAPE TO FORM
DRAW STRING
POCKET

$12\frac{3}{8}$D

$\frac{1}{2}$

$1\frac{1}{8}$

$\frac{5}{8}$

CORDUROY COVER

$\frac{9}{16}$

$3R$

$3\frac{5}{16}$

$25\frac{1}{2}$

NO. 9 WOOD SCREWS
RD. HD. 2 LG.

HALF LAP

$1\frac{1}{16}$

$\frac{5}{8}$

8

APPROXIMATELY 15
LAYERS OF VENEER

18

$1\frac{1}{8}$

FRUIT STAND

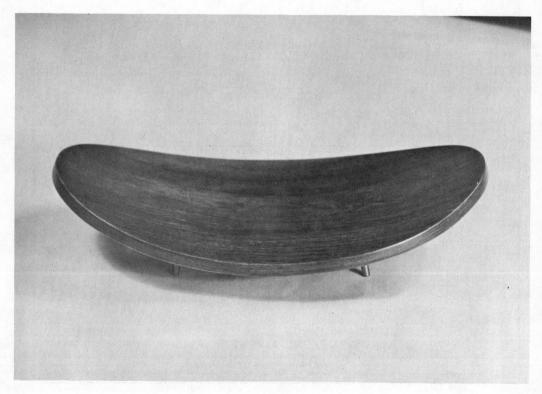

FRUIT STAND

NOTE: APPROXIMATELY 13 LAYERS
OF VENEER

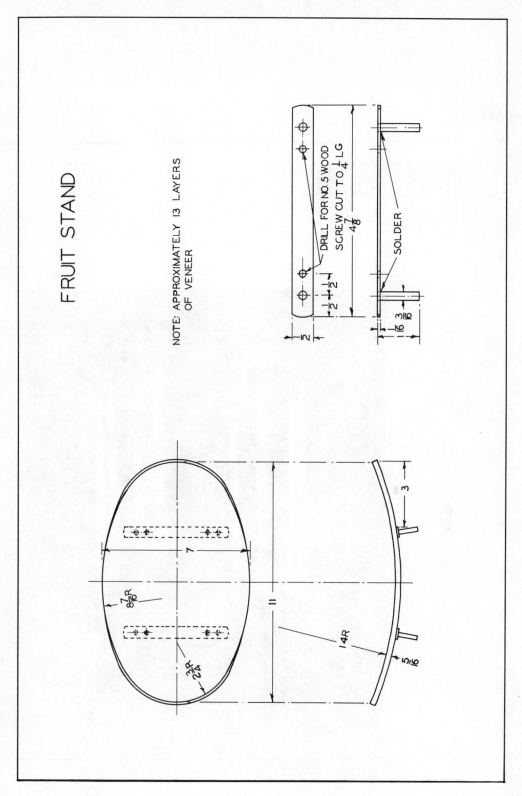

DRILL FOR NO. 5 WOOD
SCREW CUT TO $\frac{1}{4}$ LG

$4\frac{7}{8}$

SOLDER

$\frac{1}{2} + \frac{1}{2}$

$\frac{1}{2}$

$\frac{3}{16}$

7

$8\frac{7}{16}$R

$2\frac{3}{4}$R

11

14R

3

$\frac{5}{16}$

CANDLE HOLDER

CANDLE HOLDER

NOTE: THE BASE OF CANDLE HOLDER
CONSISTS OF APPROXIMATELY
22 LAYERS OF VENEER SHAPED
AS SHOWN.
RECEPTACLE IS MADE FROM
COPPER TUBE CUT TO SHAPE
INDICATED. THE RECEIVING END
IS FLARED & OPPOSITE END
IS SOLDERED TO DISC.
REQUIRED LENGTHS OF SUPPORTING
TUBES ARE CUT FROM COPPER &
SOLDERED TO UNDER SIDE OF DISC.
METAL MAY BE BUFFED OR
LACQUERED PRIOR TO INSERTING
IN BASE.

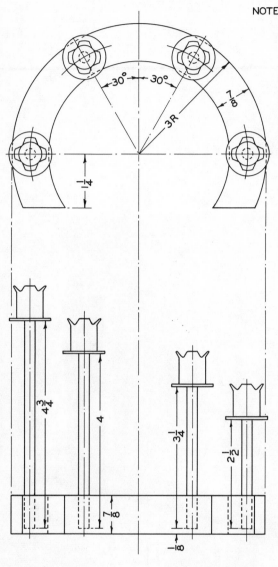

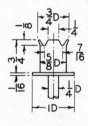

RECEPTACLE

SUGGESTED VARIATIONS

83

SALAD FORK

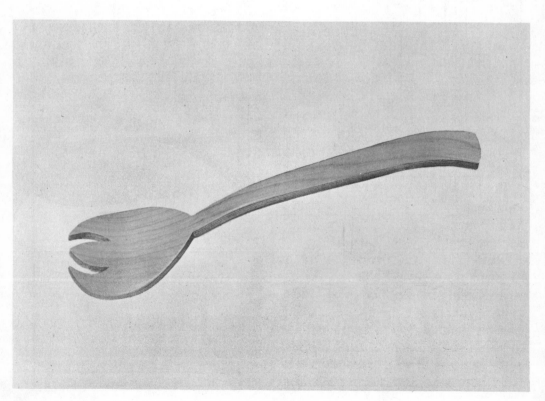

SALAD FORK

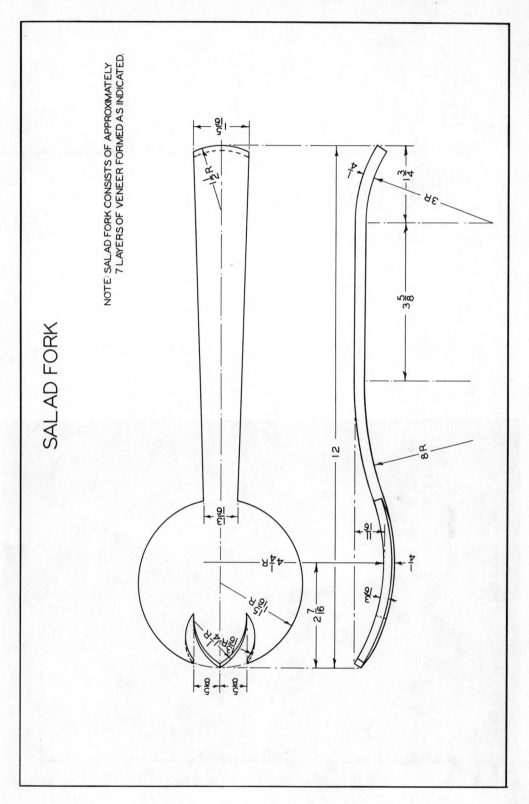

NOTE: SALAD FORK CONSISTS OF APPROXIMATELY
7 LAYERS OF VENEER FORMED AS INDICATED.

COFFEE TABLE

COFFEE TABLE

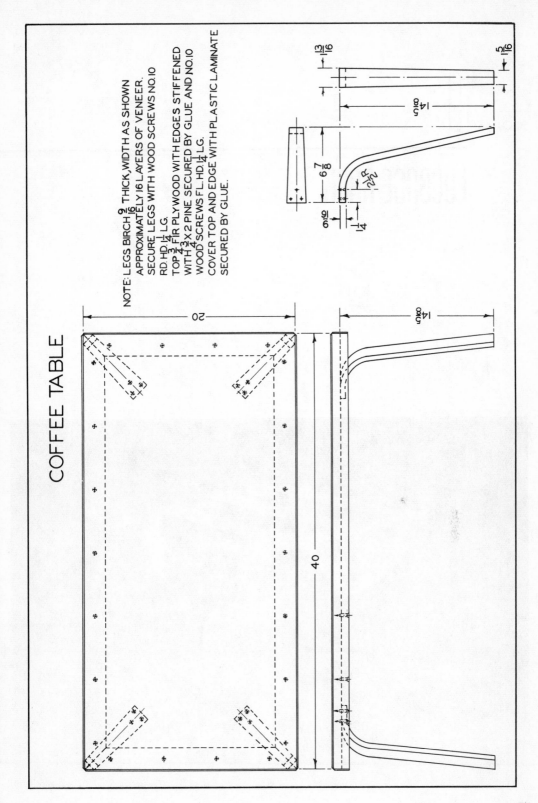

NOTE: LEGS BIRCH $\frac{9}{16}$ THICK, WIDTH AS SHOWN
APPROXIMATELY 16 LAYERS OF VENEER.
SECURE LEGS WITH WOOD SCREWS NO.10
RD. HD. $1\frac{1}{4}$ LG.
TOP $\frac{3}{4}$ FIR PLYWOOD WITH EDGES STIFFENED
WITH $\frac{3}{4}$ X 2 PINE SECURED BY GLUE AND NO.10
WOOD SCREWS FL. HD. $1\frac{1}{4}$ LG.
COVER TOP AND EDGE WITH PLASTIC LAMINATE
SECURED BY GLUE.

LUGGAGE RACK

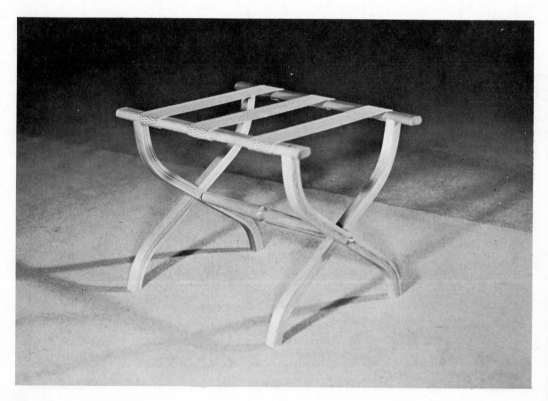

LUGGAGE RACK

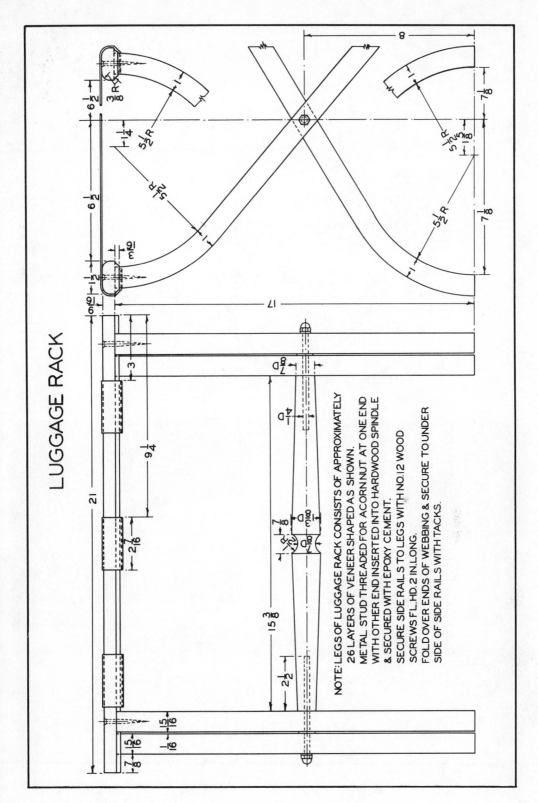

NOTE: LEGS OF LUGGAGE RACK CONSISTS OF APPROXIMATELY 26 LAYERS OF VENEER SHAPED AS SHOWN. METAL STUD THREADED FOR ACORN NUT AT ONE END WITH OTHER END INSERTED INTO HARDWOOD SPINDLE & SECURED WITH EPOXY CEMENT. SECURE SIDE RAILS TO LEGS WITH NO.12 WOOD SCREWS FL. HD. 2 IN. LONG. FOLD OVER ENDS OF WEBBING & SECURE TO UNDER SIDE OF SIDE RAILS WITH TACKS.

INDEX